GRANNA

was a

NURSE

Anna B. Crentsil

Orders
Anna B. Crentsil
www.acrentsil.wordpress.com
abcrentsil@gmail.com

ISBN 978-0-9863672-6-7
LCCN 2016941957

Book cover design and interior layout
by Judith C. Owens-Lalude
Illustrations by Anna B. Crentsil

Anike Press Louisville, KY 40241 www.AnikePress.com

This book is dedicated to the boys
and girls who want to be nurses.

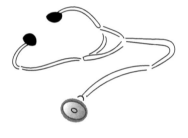

Contents

Chapter

1

Baking Brownies with Granna

Nia, who was nine-years old, stood in her Granna's kitchen.

"Could we make brownies today before my Daddy picks me up?" Nia asked.

"That would be fun," Granna said.

Granna always enjoyed baking with Nia. She looked forward to her visits.

Granna went to the pantry to look for what she needed to bake brownies. She noticed a box of brownie mix and pulled it from the shelf.

"Let's get our aprons on. We have work to do. First, let us wash our hands."

They both went to the kitchen sink to wash their hands. They dried their hands with paper towels that Granna pulled from the towel roll.

Granna cleared their cups, glasses and plates off the table to make room for the baking. Then she washed the table off.

Granna gathered the mixing bowl from the shelf in the cupboard. She got the mixing spoon and measuring cups from the cabinet drawer. She placed them on the kitchen table.

Nia stood on a stepping stool to reach the mixing bowl on the table. Granna put the ingredients close to

Nia. Nia held the mixing spoon in her right hand. Granna emptied the baking mix into the bowl. Some of the brownie mix missed the bowl. It made a brown cloud in the kitchen. Nia screamed.

"Oh, no! It looks like a chocolate cloud."

Granna laughed as she used her hands to fan the sweet-brown cloud.

"The kitchen is a smoke of chocolate flour." Granna said.

"OK, Granna, we'll have to clean this mess up."

Granna said, "Some got on the table, but enough got into the bowl."

Nia cracked two eggs. A few shell bits fell into the mix. When Nia stirred the mix, it looked like grimy-grainy goo.

"Someone will eat a brownie and have a crunchy taste when they do." Granna said.

Nia laughed and added the oil and water. Granna frowned at what she saw. Her table was smeared with brownie mix. Nia licked her mixing spoon. With one of her fingers, she wiped the mix from the bowl clean. She licked her fingers one by one. She didn't notice the mess on the table. Her hands and face were smeared with tasty dark chocolate brownie mix.

Granna put her hands on her hips. She belted, "Ha Ha. You look good enough to bake. Don't you move."

"Let's get the pan with the brownie mix into the oven,"Granna added.

While the brownies were baking, Nia pulled her stool over to the sink. Granna washed the dishes and stacked them in the sink. She told Nia stories about when she was a little girl until, the timer on the stove rang out.

"Granna, the brownies are done."

Nia looked at Granna with her wide dark brown eyes. Granna finished washing the last dish and dried her hands. She pulled the tray of brownies out of the oven and placed them on top of the range.

"Step down and move back." Granna said.

Nia did and moved her stool to the side. Granna took the pan out of the oven. She placed it on top of the stove to cool.

"Ouch!" Granna cried when she accidentally touched the hot pan. She pulled her hand back. The brownies nearly fell on the floor. "I think I burned my hand."

"Let me help, Granna."

Granna shoved her hand under cold running water. Nia looked at Granna's hand. "There is no blood. There is no cut. I do see a little redness. Keep it under the cold water a little longer, Granna."

Nia gently dried Granna's hand with a clean soft cloth.

"You will be a good nurse. You took good care of my hand."Granna explained.

Nia pulled her stool close to the stove and stood on it.

"Um. These smell good."

"The brownies look good enough to eat," Nia said.

"Yes, they do, but let's wait until they cool. We don't want to burn our fingers or mouth."

"OK, I'll read your book, Granna, until they are ready."

Nia looked at her Granna with her large brown eyes.

"Granna, tell me about what you did when you used to work?"

Granna, pushed her bifocal eyeglasses up on her nose. She looked down at Nia. She took her by the hand.

"Come with me. Let's sit down. But first, let me finish cleaning the brownie goo off the table. It's sticky with mix, eggs, oil, and water."

When Granna finished, she turned and said, "Follow me outside. The brownies can wait while we talk."

Chapter

2

Nursing Jobs

Nia and Granna sat outside on the steps. At first, they watched the birds fly about, the butterflies flutter about, and squirrels jump from tree limb to tree limb.

"There is a lot to see when you sit still."

"I know Granna," Nia said.

Nia leaned toward Granna, she looked into her eyes. "What are those lines in your eyeglasses?" She asked.

"These are old people's eyeglasses; they call them bifocals."

"Did your doctor give you those glasses?"

"No, he didn't give them to me. The eye doctor is an ophthalmologist. He prescribed them for me. Just like your eye doctor prescribed your glasses for you."

"Granna, you know a lot about doctors. Tell me, what did you do when you worked?"

"I was a registered nurse. I did all kinds of nursing jobs."

"Were they difficult?"

"Nurses work hard but they love what they do. They are also called healthcare workers. Some are called teachers, clinicians and practitioners."

"What are clinicians and practitioners? I have never heard of those words."

"Clinicians are nurses who work in a special area in the hospital; such as a pediatric nurse. This nurse takes care of children. The orthopedic nurse takes care of patients with broken bones. Some clinicians also work as nurse managers in the hospital or teachers in college. They have special training for those jobs. All nurses teach. There are too many jobs that nurses do, to name them all."

"Let me tell you about the Practitioners. They go to school for more training. They usually attend college to specialize as Family, Pediatric, or OB & GYN Nurse Practitioners. They practice like a doctor but with the supervision of a doctor close by. The obstetrics and gynecologist nurse practitioner work with pregnant females and other non-pregnant females. We call them OB&GYN Nurse Practitioners. Family Nurse Practitioner takes care of the whole family; the woman, man, boys, girls, and babies. Some practitioners practice like doctors. They work out of their own clinics.

"What does supervise mean?"

"It means that the doctor will be available to look over and check their work when needed."

14

Chapter

What Do Nurses Do?

"What else do nurses do?"

"Nurses have many responsibilities. They are challenging. Many nurses help people get better. Sometimes they give medications and shots to patients. They help doctors in the hospitals, nursing homes and clinics to take care of patients. They clean wounds with medications and dress them, too."

"Dress them? Like with doll clothes?"

"Oh, no. they use bandages."

"Okay, Granna. What else do nurses do?"

"Well, let me think…. Oh, yes. They help prevent and treat diseases, illnesses, and injuries.

When you go to the hospital, doctor's office or clinic, nurses are usually the first people who see you. He or she will use a thermometer to take your temperature. They also put a blood pressure cuff around your arm to check your blood pressure. With the stethoscope, they also can listen to your heart and breathing sounds.

Nurses teach students in nursing school. They also teach family members in hospitals, clinics and their homes–and patients in their homes. They visit students in grade school, middle school, and high school to tell them about health and safety. They also check their school health records for up to date immunizations."

"Granna, that's a lot for nurses to do. Now, I understand why you talk about being clean. Nurses have to be clean and have clean hands. They want to keep from spreading germs from one person to the next."

"Nia, do you remember when I took care of my mother?"

"Yes, and you also took care of me and my brother when we were sick. You always washed your hands to keep from getting sick and reminded us to do the same. I remember when we came in from playing outside. You'd say, "Wash your hand before you poison yourself."

"Ha Ha," Granna and Nia both laughed.

Nia became excited about the jobs of nurses. She felt that she could become a nurse.

Nia ran to get her helmet and scooter. She shouted. "I'm racing to be a nurse now."

Granna smiled and said, "Hold on Nia! You can't hurry to be a nurse. First, you have to grow up. Then you must go to school to learn how to become a nurse, practice being one, and then become one," she said.

"I will grow up and go to nursing school. I will keep clean and take care of myself and my doll, too."

"Do you know why people get sick?" Granna asked.

Nia said, "Yes, if they don't wash their hands."

"True, because you touch many things with your hands. You may get germs from them. When you put your hands in your mouth or rub your nose and eyes, those germs can make you sick."

"Granna, you can help children learn about nursing. You can also teach the importance of being clean."

"Children are always on the move. You and your brother take part in sports. You both play soccer and swim. You play tennis, and go to dance lessons. Your brother plays baseball and takes karate lessons, too. These sports can cause injuries and pass on germs. When team members share their water bottles, they also share their germs. When they share their hats, caps and helmets, they share their germs. Their heads can get infections or they get head lice. If they don't wear a helmet, shin guard or athletic cup they can get hurt. You have to be careful when you ride your bicycles or scooters. Follow the rules and be safe."

Granna said, "I wrote a healthcare guide for boys and girls. It will help them to prevent illnesses, injuries and diseases."

Nia asked. "Can I have one?"

"You sure can."

"I'll share it with my Mommy, Daddy, my brother and all my friends. They'll learn about what nurses do. They'll even learn that it is important to wash their hands. And they will learn how to be safe when they play."

"We better go back in the house to check on the brownies. I can still smell them."

"They smell good. They should be cool by now. I want to have ice cream with mine."

Nia and Granna washed their hands.

Chapter

Nia Going Home

Nia finished her ice cream and brownies.
The doorbell rang.

"This was a good treat, Granna."

"Let me see who is at the door," Granna
said.

Nia followed Granna to the door.

"It's Daddy, Mommy and Gerard!"

Granna was surprised to see Nia's parents and her brother, Gerard so soon.

"Hi Granna", Gerard said.

"Hello, Momma," Nia's Mommy said.

"Hello Granna," Nia's Daddy said.

Granna said, "Hello, and what a surprise? Come in, and join us in the kitchen."

"Hi Mommy, Daddy and Gerard, I baked brownies." Nia shouted.

She ran to the kitchen. Everyone followed her to the kitchen.

"They smell good and look good," Mommy said.

Nia said, "We were waiting for them to cool down. Granna burned her hand."

"Momma, are you alright?" Nia's Mommy asked.

"Oh, yes. My little Nia was a very good nurse today. She took good care of me."

"Are the brownies ready for us to eat now?" Gerard asked.

Granna said, "Yes, I will take a couple for me and Papa. We know how much he likes Nia's brownies.

"You can take the rest home. Your Mommy and Daddy are in a hurry."

"Granna wrote a book on how to be a nurse, keep clean, and be safe. She gave me one for all of us to read."

"Don't forget to take it with you." Granna said.

Nia hugged Granna and whispered in her ear. "I love you, Granna."

Daddy, Mommy and Gerard said, "Thanks Granna."

They all went home carrying their brownies and book.

Health
&
Safety
GUIDE
for
BOYS AND GIRLS

How to Take Care of Your Body

Head

1. Wash your hair with a gentle shampoo.

2. Don't share combs, brush, hats, caps or any other types of head pieces.

3. Keep your hair well-groomed by combing and or brushing it everyday.

Eyes

1. Have your eye checked by a doctor.

2. Never put a sharp object near your eyes, ears, nose or mouth.

3. Don't wear someone else's glasses or contact lens.

Nose

1. Use clean tissue when cleaning inside your nose.

2. Cover your nose when sneezing.

3. Blow your nose with clean tissue and wash hands afterward.

Mouth

1. Brush teeth daily and use mouthwash as instructed.

2. See a dentist to have your teeth cleaned to prevent cavities.

3. Use a lip balm when your lips are dry and cracking.

4. Use a mouth guard when playing contact sports.

5. Don't run with something in your mouth.

Face

1. Keep your face clean by washing it everyday. This will aid in preventing oil and dirt built up that can cause acne.

2. Consult your doctor for over the counter acne medications.

Body

1. Shower or take a bath everyday.

2. Use soaps designed for bathing.

3. Use deodorant, if needed, after cleaning your armpits thoroughly with soap and warm water.

4. Dry yourself well. Use a lotion for arms, legs and other body parts to prevent skin dryness.

Feet

1. Keep feet clean and use a lotion to keep them soft.

2. Wear clean socks everyday to prevent athlete's feet.

3. Wear shoes when going outside to protect feet.

Clothing

1. Do not wear dirty clothes.

2. Change your underwear everyday to prevent bad odor and infections.

3. Wear clothing that is right for the weather.

How to be Safe & Healthy

Bedroom

1. Windows: Keep closed and locked. Use screens in spring and summer to keep out insects.

2. Night lights: Use for safety when going to bathroom at night.

3. Doors: If there is a fire, touch the door and the doorknob. If one of them is hot or warm, don't open the door. If the door knob is cool and you don't see smoke around the door you can open it.

4. Toys: Pick up your toys from the floor after you play with them to prevent falls.

Foods

1. Temperature: Allow hot foods to cool before you eat to not get burned.

2. Allergy: Take your allergy medication as prescribed. Don't take other people's medications. Don't eat foods you are allergic to.

3. Knives: Use knives with the help of an adult when you want to cut up foods.

4. Food: Daily foods that help you to be healthy are: milk, fruits, cereal, eggs, vegetables, and

meat. They will also help you to grow and develop strong bones and healthy teeth.

5. Water: Drink plenty of water especially during sports and other activities.

Hiking

1. Weather: Check the weather before you dress to go out.

2. Clothing: Wear a sweater or a coat when the weather is cold. When it is hot dress light. If it's raining, wear a rain coat and boots.

3. Shoes: Wear sport shoes or tennis shoes for running, jumping and, hiking.

4. Snacks: Take along a snack and something to drink when hiking or walking a long distance.

5. Flashlight: Check the batteries often so the flashlight is ready when it's needed.

6. Telephone: Take important telephone numbers with you when you go hiking.

7. Buddy System: Always hike in a group with an adult and carry a cell phone.

Skin Care

1. Lotions: Use creamy lotion for your skin. Ask your parents to help you to pick one.

2. Creams: Use the creams given to you by a doctor or parent.

3. Insect repellent: Use an insect repellent when you're going into a wooded areas. Ask the drug store pharmacist which one is best for you.

Playground

1. Safety: Always be with someone you know. Don't talk to strangers.

2. Safety: Remember to report any unwanted physical contact from a child or grownup. Let the person know that you don't want them to touch you. Shout, "STOP!" and run away from them.

Sleep

1. Proper sleep: You should sleep 8 to 10 hours every night.

2. Naps: Take a nap during the day if you feel tired.

3. Sleep: Lack of sleep can cause tiredness in the middle of the day. You won't feel your best or

do your best in school if you are not well rested.

Sports

1. Safety equipment such as helmets, swim caps, and baseball caps should not be shared. You can get head lice when you do.

2. Padding: Use safety pads when you play football and shin guards when playing lacrosse and soccer.

3. Use a mouth guard when playing basketball and football.

Toys

1. Bicycle: Wear a helmet when you ride your bike.

2. Scooters: Wear a helmet when you're on a scooter.

3. Skates: Wear a helmet, knee pads, and elbow pads when you go roller skating.

4. Objects: Don't put anything in your mouth other than food. If you are not sure ask a grownup.

IMPORTANT Information & TELEPHONE NUMBERS

LEARN THIS INFORMATION

Home Phone Number

( ) _____ - _____

Home Address

Street _____

Building _____ Apt. _____

City _____ State _____

ZipCode_____ Postal Code _____

POST THESE NUMBERS
(copy, cutout, laminate, and post)

Emergency - 911

Poison Control 1-800-222-1222

Mom's work number
( ) ____ - _____

Dad's work number
( ) ____ - _____

National Pediatrics Child Abuse
(614) 744-3278

IMPORTANT TELEPHONE NUMBERS

Mother's Mobile Phone Number

( ) _____ - _____

Dad's Mobile Phone Number

( ) _____ - _____

Grandmother's Mobile Phone Number

( ) _____ - _____

Grandfather's Mobile Phone Number

( ) _____ - _____

Aunt _____ Mobile Phone Number

( ) _____ - _____

Uncle _____ Mobile Phone Number

( ) _____ - _____

Older Cousin
( ) _____ - _____

_____ Mobile Phone Number

Neighbor's Phone Number

( ) _____ - _____

Legal Guardian

( ) _____ - _____

Glossary

Accident: an unfortunate or unplanned event

Acne: A skin condition that results from clogging up or blocking the oil glands in the skin. This causes inflammation and red pimples on the face, back, or chest.

Allergy: Conditions that cause people to sneeze, cough, develop a rash or have another unpleasant reaction. People could react to dust, pollen, foods, dog and cat dander and other things.

Athlete's Foot: An itchy rash that can develop on your feet and between your toes. Athlete's foot is caused by a fungus and is usually treated by applying special creams or ointments to the rash.

Balm: An ointment, salve or cream. Used for comfort or relief of dryness on the lips.

Bifocals: Eye glasses or lenses that have two sections. One for seeing up close and the other farther away.

Blood pressure: The force of blood as it flows through a person's body.

Buddy System: Having a close friend or pals who will be with you on your adventure in life.

Cavity: A hole or hollow space in something solid, such as a tooth.

Challenge: Something difficult that requires extra work or effort to do a task.

Chart: Medical information about a patient.

Clinician: A doctor or nurse who works directly with patients.

Communication: Share information, ideas, or feelings with another person.

Counter: A long flat surface, as in the kitchen or department store.

Cream: A thick smooth substance that you put on your skin.

Cupboard: A cabinet or closet for storing dishes, food, etc.

Cuff: A band that is filled with air and wrapped around an arm to measure blood pressure.

Daily: Everyday.

Degree: A unit to measure temperature.

Dentist: Someone who is trained to examine, clean, and take care of teeth.

Development: To build on something or make something grow.

Difficult: Not easy.

Disease: A specific illness.

Drops: A small quantity of liquid, as in eye drops.

Emergency: A sudden and dangerous situation that must be dealt with quickly.

Encourage: To give someone confidence by praising or supporting the person.

Fluids: flowing or liquid.

Gear: Equipment or clothing; such as football helmet.

Germs: Tiny living things that can cause illnesses.

Growth: The process of growing; increase.

Gynecologist: The doctor who takes care of woman's health

Healthcare: The business of working to help people stay well and healthy.

Helmet: A hard hat that protects your head during sports or danger.

Hydrate: To give fluids or water.

Illness: Sick

Infection: An illness caused by germs.

Ingredient: Parts, items and things to add to a mixture.

Lice: Small insects without wings that live on animals or people.

Lotion: A thin cream that is used to clean, soften or heal the skin.

Manager: Someone in charge.

Manual: A book of instructions that tells you how to do something.

Measure: To determine the size, weight, etc. of something.

Mitten: A covering of the hands.

Nursing: To care for sick or injured people.

Ointment: A thick, often greasy substance put on the skin to heal or protect it.

Ophthalmologist: The doctor who studies and treats conditions of the eyes.

Orthopedic Nurse: The nurse who takes care of patients with broken bones.

Padding: Cotton, foam rubber, or any other soft material used as cushioning for protection or comfort.

Pediatric Nurse: This nurse takes care of children

Performance: The way something works.

Poison: A substance that can kill or harm someone if it is swallowed, inhaled, or sometimes even touched.

Practitioner: A person who is educated and experienced in a clinical area.

Prescription: An order for drugs or medicine written by a doctor or nurse practitioner to treat a patient.

Prevent: To stop something from happening.

Problem: A difficult situation that needs to be figured out or overcome.

Proper: Right or suitable for a given purpose or occasion.

Registered: To be documented or official.

Requirement: Something that you need to do or is necessary to have.

Routine: A regular way or pattern of doing things.

Specialize: To focus on one area of work, or to learn a lot about one subject.

Stethoscope: A tool used to listen to the heart and lungs.

Supervisor: Someone who watches over and directs the work of other people.

Temperature: The measurement of heat and cold.

Treat: To try to cure or heal, to give medical attention to.

Tissue: Soft, thin paper used for wiping, and wrapping.

Wound: An injury or cut.

Young
Anna B. Crentsil

as a nurse

1974 circa

Anna B. Crentsil

... grew up in Louisville, Kentucky. As a child she wanted to be a nurse and used her teddy bears as her patients. After graduating from Indiana University School of Nursing, she became a registered nurse. In her more than forty years of nursing and as a military wife, she worked in different areas of nursing. She worked in Medical-Surgical, Psychiatry, Operating Room, and Labor and Delivery. She has done Public Health Nursing. She taught Maternal and Pediatric Nursing in a vocational nursing program and also taught in the Indianapolis Public Schools as a substitute teacher.

She is married and has three grown children and two grandchildren.

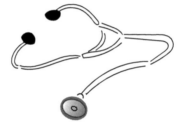

Made in the USA
Lexington, KY
26 May 2018